HOW WELL DO YOU KNOW YOUR SHAKESPEARE ?

ALAN DENT

Forty sets of Questions and Answers

MACDONALD : LONDON

First published in 1964 by
Macdonald & Co. (Publishers) Ltd.,
Gulf House, 2 Portman Street, London, W.1

Made and printed in Great Britain by
Dawson & Goodall, Ltd.,
Grove Street, Bath, Somerset

Dedicated to

IVOR BROWN

Critic,

Scholar,

and Friend

who knows all the answers

OVER AND ABOVE

What play contains—

(1) a Jew besides Shylock?

(2) only two Women, and both of them in a single short scene?

(3) a Moor other than Othello and Aaron (in *Titus Andronicus*)?

(4) a Witch other than those in *Macbeth*?

(5) a Paris besides Juliet's suitor?

(6) a Black Child?

(7) a Bloody Child?

(8) a Pandar other than Pandarus?

(9) a Scotsman outside *Macbeth*?

(10) a Welshman over and above Fluellen, Sir Hugh Evans and Owen Glendower?

NON-APPEARING CHARACTERS

Which plays have references to these persons who do not actually appear, and what is each by profession or relationship?

(1) Nedar

(2) Rosaline

(3) Lamond

(4) Barbara

(5) Sycorax

(6) Davy Gam, esquire

(7) Flibbertigibbet

(8) Susan ("now with God")

(9) Susan Grindstone and Nell

(10) Gerard de Narbon

FOOTMEN AND ATTENDANTS

Which plays have the following servants or attendants, and whom do they serve or attend?

(1) James Gurney

(2) Curio

(3) Peter

(4) Curtis

(5) Reynaldo

(6) Boyet

(7) Pisanio

(8) Lucius

(9) Seyton

(10) Adam

PLACES FOR PLAYS

What plays happen in—

(1) Vienna?

(2) Navarre?

(3) Messina?

(4) Sicily and Bohemia?

(5) Venice and Cyprus?

(6) Verona and Milan and Mantua?

(7) Rousillon, Paris, Florence and Marseilles?

(8) Northampton, Angiers, Bury St. Edmunds and Swinstead Abbey?

(9) Dispersedly—all over the Eastern Mediterranean?

(10) An island without a name?

GUARDIANS OF THE LAW

Which plays have these Constables, Gaolers, Executioners, Officers of the Watch and the like?

(1) Verges

(2) Dull

(3) Hugh Oatcake

(4) Fang

(5) Abhorson

(6) Elbow

(7) George Seacoal

(8) Snare

(9) Dogberry

(10) The Lord High Constable of France

OATHS AND UTTERANCES

Who swears by—

(1) St. Anne?

(2) St. Paul?

(3) St. Patrick?

(4) God's Sonties?

(5) Gis and St. Charity?

(6) Apollo?

(7) Yonder Sacred Moon?

(8) The Sacred Radiance of the Sun?

(9) Jacob's Staff?

(10) The Very Fangs of Malice?

ALL IN ONE

Who and in what play . . .

(1) gate-crashed at a picnic?

(2) was threatened by both a lioness and a green and gilded snake?

(3) carved verses on tree-trunks?

(4) called herself Aliena?

(5) was ambitious for a motley coat?

(6) had his mouth full of news?

(7) found good in everything?

(8) thanked the gods she was foul?

(9) was more than common tall?

(10) had inky brows, black silk hair, bugle eyeballs, and cheeks of cream, and was told to thank heaven, fasting, for a good man's love?

ENDS OF LIVES

Who died as follows?

(1) babbling o' green fields
(2) of snake-bite
(3) by hanging
(4) by smothering (on stage)
(5) by decapitation
(6) by swallowing fire
(7) by public assassination
(8) by public lynching
(9) by being stabbed through an arras
(10) by being cut to pieces at his own request

SUITES AND CLUSTERS

What groups are these and in what plays are they found?

(1) Maud, Bridget, Marian, Cicely, Gillian, Ginn

(2) Tray, Blanch and Sweetheart

(3) Nathaniel, Joseph, Nicholas, Philip, Walter and Sugarsop

(4) Moll, Meg, Marian and Margery . . . and Kate

(5) Bushey, Bagot, Green and the Earl of Wiltshire

(6) Mouldy, Shadow, Wart, Feeble and Bullcalf

(7) Little John Doit, black George Barnes, Francis Pickbone and Will Squele

(8) George Bevis, John Holland, Dick the Butcher, Smith the Weaver, and Michael

(9) Simon Catling, Hugh Rebeck and James Soundpost

(10) Peaseblossom, Cobweb, Moth and Mustardseed

STARTS AND FRAGMENTS

Who sings or utters these snatches of song, starts of unfinished stories, invocations and the like?

(1) Child Rowland to the dark tower came . . .

(2) Ducdamé, ducdamé, ducdamé!

(3) O the twelfth day of December!

(4) And will he not come again? . . .

(5) The ouzel cock so black of hue . . .

(6) King Stephen was a worthy peer . . .

(7) Do nothing but eat, and make good cheer . . .

(8) Jog on, jog on the footpath way . . .

(9) Farewell, dear heart, since I must needs be gone . . .

(10) There was a man dwelt by a churchyard . . .

IMMORTAL GODS

Which characters in what plays refer to the classical gods? For example:—

(1) Who said he had "fierce affections", and thought what Venus did with Mars?

(2) Who asked Apollo, Pallas, Jove or Mercury to inspire him?

(3) Who said his "imaginations" were "as foul as Vulcan's stithy"?

(4) Who swore by the simplicity of Venus' doves?

(5) What were "sweeter than the lids of Juno's eyes, or Cytherea's breath"?

(6) Who rose from the ground like feather'd Mercury?

(7) Who was described by whom as "sport for Jove"?

(8) Who "wear yet upon their chins the beards of Hercules and frowning Mars"?

(9) Who sat with whom on Neptune's yellow sands?

(10) Whose "pudency was so rosy that the sweet view on't might well have warmed old Saturn"?

BACKGROUND EXTRAS

What plays contain these groups of subsidiaries?

(1)   Reapers in a Masque

(2)   Gravediggers

(3)   Rebels

(4)   Aediles and Lictors

(5)   Falconers

(6)   Gardeners

(7)   Fishermen

(8)   Shepherdesses

(9)   Mariners

(10)   Amazons in a Masque

CLERICS AND CHURCHMEN

What plays have these Prelates or Clergymen as characters?

(1) The Archbishop of Canterbury

(2) Cardinal Pandulph, Papal Legate

(3) The Bishop of Carlisle

(4) Cardinal Wolsey

(5) Cardinal Campeius

(6) The Bishop of Ely (two of them)

(7) Cardinal Bourchier

(8) The Bishop of Winchester

(9) Sir Hugh Evans, a parson

(10) Sir Oliver Martext, a country vicar

DRAMATIS PERSONAE

In "A Midsummer Night's Dream"—

(1) Who were the six members of the Athenian Thespians?

(2) What were their first names (one of them has none!)?

(3) What were their respective professions?

(4) What parts in their production were they respectively offered at the first rehearsal?

(5) What parts, respectively, did they finally play?

[Double marks]

SITES AND BACKGROUNDS

Which play has a scene or scenes set in or on—

(1)   a Moated Grange?

(2)   a Blasted Heath?

(3)   an Orchard in Gloucestershire?

(4)   a Cave in Wales?

(5)   a Cave near a Seashore in Greece?

(6)   an Inn-yard at Rochester?

(7)   a Shepherd's Fair?

(8)   Blackheath?

(9)   the country near Dover?

(10) Kimbolton in Huntingdonshire?

ODD FEATURES

What plays have these unusual features?

(1)   a man chased by a bear

(2)   a statue which comes to life

(3)   a duet sung by two page boys

(4)   a dirge sung by two brothers

(5)   an interrupted wedding

(6)   an interrupted funeral

(7)   a supper where nothing is eaten

(8)   a supper where there is nothing to eat

(9)   a banquet interrupted by a ghost

(10)   a feast of human flesh

TRADES AND CALLINGS

In which plays do you find these characters, named and unnamed?

(1) a Wrestler

(2) a Goldsmith

(3) a Schoolmaster

(4) a Jeweller

(5) a Boatswain

(6) a Bellows-mender

(7) a French physician

(8) a Prisoner condemned to Death

(9) an Eunuch

10) a Clown who brings Figs

SOUBRIQUETS

Who bore these nicknames or aliases, and in what plays?

(1) Robin Goodfellow

(2) Sir Topas

(3) Ganymede

(4) Fidele

(5) Bully

(6) Poor Tom

(7) Cesario

(8) Morgan

(9) Polydore

(10) Cadwal

A CLUSTER OF FELLOWS

Who are these fellows, and who so described them?

(1) A fellow of the strangest mind i' the world

(2) A fellow of infinite jest, of most excellent fancy

(3) A fellow almost damn'd in a fair wife

(4) A marvellous witty fellow, I assure you

(5) A very tainted fellow, and full of wickedness

(6) A woodland fellow, sir, that always loved a great fire

(7) A good-limbed fellow; young, strong, and of good friends

(8) A barren-spirited fellow; one that feeds on abjects, orts and imitations

(9) A rural fellow that will not be denied your highness' presence

(10) An honest fellow enough, and one that loves quails; but he has not so much brains as ear-wax

FATHERS   WANTED

Who was the father of each of these characters?

(1)   Hamlet

(2)   Desdemona

(3)   Hermia

(4)   King Henry V

(5)   Katharine and Bianca

(6)   Hero

(7)   Perdita

(8)   Miranda

(9)   Celia

(10)   Imogen

MOTHERS   WANTED

And who was the mother of each of these?

  (1) Juliet

  (2) Mamillius

  (3) Coriolanus

  (4) Cloten

  (5) Richard, Duke of Gloucester

  (6) Jessica

  (7) Susan ("now with God")

  (8) Arthur, Duke of Bretagne

  (9) Hamlet

 (10) Romeo

FOOD AND DRINK

In matters of eating and drinking, who and in what play—

(1) was fed "with apricocks and dewberries"?

(2) were promised scamels (i.e. sea-mew chicks) by whom?

(3) was "given to fornications, and to taverns, and sack and wine"?

(4) drank wine "to the general joy o' the whole table"?

(5) thought of drinking hot blood?

(6) was partial to pickle-herring?

(7) had "very poor and unhappy brains for drinking"?

(8) was said to have eaten "strange flesh" in the wars?

(9) munched chestnuts?

(10) swallowed "the old **rat** and the ditch-dog" and drank "the green mantle of the standing pool"?

DOG'S ABUSE

Who is called these names to his face, or behind his back, and by whom?

(1) a devil's butcher

(2) a dreadful minister of hell

(3) a lump of foul deformity

(4) a diffus'd infection of a man

(5) a troubler of the poor world's peace

(6) an elvish-mark'd, abortive, rooting hog

(7) a slander of his mother's heavy womb and loathed issue of his father's loins!

(8) a hell-hound that doth hunt us all to death

(9) a bottled spider, a foul hunch-back'd toad

(10) a bloody dog now dead

FIRST WORDS

What plays begin thus—

(1)   with the words, "Nay, but . . ."?

(2)   with the question, " Who's there? . . ."?

(3)   with the words, "As I remember . . ."?

(4)   with the command to the audience, "Open your ears!"?

(5)   with the line, "So shaken as we are, so wan with care"?

(6)   with the line, "In sooth, I know not why I am so sad"?

(7)   with the line, "In delivering my son from me, I bury a second husband"?

(8)   with the order, "Hence! home, you idle creatures, get you home!"

(9)   with a Prologue in the form of a Sonnet?

(10)   with a Funeral in Westminster Abbey?

LAST WORDS

And what plays conclude thus—

(1) with a Dead March and the single word, "Assist" (in a line by itself)?

(2) with a Dance preceded by the words, "Strike up, pipers!" spoken by the hero?

(3) with a six-line Epilogue spoken by a King of France, concluding, "Your gentle hands lead us, and take our hearts"?

(4) with Songs of Spring and Winter, and the conclusion:—"The words of Mercury are harsh after the songs of Apollo. You, that way: we, this way"?

(5) with a Song beginning with the line, " When that I was and a little tiny boy"?

(6) with the line, "One feast, one house, one mutual happiness"?

(7) with an Epilogue in prose, spoken by the heroine?

(8) with a Dead March after the words, "Go bid the soldiers shoot"?

(9) with an Invitation to a Coronation?

(10) with a Dead March after the words, "The oldest hath borne most; we that are young Shall never see so much, nor live so long"?

CATS AND DOGS

(1) Who was described as "more than prince of cats"?

(2) Who described himself as "a dog at a catch"?

(3) Who was "as vigilant as a cat to steal cream"?

(4) Who called his dog "the sourest natured dog that lives"?

(5) Who wanted to play "a part to tear a cat in"?

(6) Who was called, and by whom, "an Iceland dog—a prick-eared cur of Iceland"?

(7) Who talked of the antipathy of some persons to "a harmless necessary cat"?

(8) Who was called, and by whom, "thou issue of a mangey dog"?

(9) Who said: "The cat will mew, and dog will have his day"?

(10) Who declared he would rather be "a dog, a mule, a cat, a fitchew, a toad, a lizard, an owl, a puttock, or a herring without a roe" than a certain cuckolded husband?

THREE BIRDS

Where does the Lark?

(1) at heaven's gate sing
(2) from his moist cabinet mount up on high
(3) chant tirra-lirra
(4) sing where night-owls shriek
(5) sing out of tune, straining hard discords and unpleasing sharps

And where does the Eagle?

(6) o'er his aëry tower
(7) suffer little birds to sing, and is not careful what they mean thereby

And who, on the subject of the Wren?

(8)   compared a drop of pity to a wren's eye
(9)   was called the youngest wren of nine
(10) observed that the poor wren, the most diminutive of birds, will fight—her young ones in the nest—against the owl

LESSER FRY

*In which plays do you find these minor characters, all un-
named?*

(1)   a Dutch Gentleman

(2)   a Tailor

(3)   a Sexton

(4)   a Town Crier

(5)   a Bawd

(6)   a Son that killed his Father

(7)   a Father that killed his Son

(8)   an Old Widow of Florence

(9)   a Sea Captain

(10) a Spanish Gentleman

HUSBANDS OF HEROINES

Who in the end—and in what play—married these young ladies:

(1) Beatrice

(2) Audrey

(3) Celia

(4) Hermia

(5) Isabella

(6) Maria

(7) Mariana

(8) Miranda

(9) Perdita

(10) Portia

GOLD AND SILVER

(1) Whose chamber was "hang'd with tapestry of silk and silver"?

(2) Whose "golden touch could soften steel and stones"?

(3) Whose beard was likened, and by whom, to "a sable silver'd"?

(4) Who addressed his father's crown:—"O polished perturbation, golden care!"?

(5) Who were said (by whom?) to "fleet the time carelessly as they did in the golden world"?

(6) Whose sunny locks were said to "hang on her temples like a golden fleece"?

(7) Who was left "seven hundred pounds of moneys, and gold, and silver"?

(8) Whose "silver skin" was said to be "laced with his golden blood"?

(9) For whom was ordered "a silver basin full of rose-water"?

(10) "What says the silver with her virgin hue?"— and where?—and to whom?

FISHY ONES

(1) Who was said to have been "groping for trouts in a peculiar river"?

(2) Who was described as "a trout that must be caught with tickling"?

(3) Who "never was so frail to change the cod's head for a salmon's tail"?

(4) Who declared:—"There is a river in Macedon; and there is also moreover a river at Monmouth . . . and there is salmons in both"?

(5) Where did the "maw and gulf of the ravin'd salt-sea shark" end up?

(6) Who hiccuped and said:—"A plague o' these pickle-herrin'!"?

(7) Who had "an alligator stuff'd and other skins of ill-shaped fishes"?

(8) "When he beheld his shadow in the brook The fishes spread on it their golden gills"— Who was this?

(9) Who was called "a Triton of the minnows"—by whom?

(10) Who was said, by whom, to have had "a very ancient and fish-like smell"?

DOUBLE-BARRELLED ADJECTIVES

Who first used at whom or what these double-barrelled epithets?

(1) nook-shotten

(2) urchin-snouted

(3) orange-tawny

(4) grim-visaged

(5) blood-boltered

(6) sodden-witted

(7) plague-sore

(8) evil-eyed

(9) red-hipped

(10) palpable-gross

DISORDERS AND DISEASES

Who suffered from—

(1)   the toothache?

(2)   chronic dermatitis brought about by poison unusually administered?

(3)   a fistula?

(4)   a severe cold in the head ("a salt and sorry rheum")?

(5)   aching eyes ("Does that bode weeping?")

(6)   "a rheum in his eyes, and such an ache in his bones"?

(7)   flatulence, or at least hiccups?

(8)   "lethargies, cold palsies, raw eyes, dirt-rotten livers, wheezing lungs, bladders full of imposthume, sciaticas, limestones i' the palm, incurable bone-ache"?

And what two characters (four in all)

(9)   go mad?

(10) pretend to go mad?

VARIOUS FRUITS

(1) Who loved long life better than figs?

(2) Who called for dates and quinces in the pantry?

(3) Who asked for some strawberries from whose garden?

(4) Who picked out from the London mob "the youths that thunder at a play-house and fight for bitten apples"?

(5) Who was as crest-fallen as a dried pear?

(6) Whose grandam would give him a plum, a cherry, and a fig?

(7) Who ordered for her belovèd "purple grapes, green figs, and mulberries"?

(8) What was not worth a gooseberry?

(9) Who asked his apprentice to tie up "dangling apricocks"?

(10) Whose wife desired some damsons and made him climb for them to danger of his life?

MAIDS-IN-WAITING

Whom do these Maids and Ladies-in-Waiting attend on, and in which plays?—

(1) Emilia

(2) Patience

(3) Maria

(4) Ursula

(5) Alice

(6) Lucetta

(7) Nerissa

(8) Iras

(9) Helen—and

(10) another Emilia

QUEENS—NAMED AND UNNAMED

In what plays, and under what names, do these Queens find themselves?

(1)   Queen of the Amazons

(2)   Queen of the Fairies

(3)   Queen of the Goths

Where are?

(4)   Queen Gertrude

(5)   Queen Elinor

(6)   Queen Katharine

(7)   Queen Isabel (of France) and a

(8)   Queen Elizabeth other than *the* Queen Elizabeth

(9) and (10), two unnamed English Queens—one actual and one legendary

ALL IN NAVARRE

Which particular play contains these characters, and what are their names?

(1) a King

(2) a Princess

(3) a Forester

(4) a Schoolmaster

(5) a Constable

(6) a Clown

(7) a Curate

(8) a Country Wench

(9) a Page

(10) a Fantastical Spaniard

[Note: Since neither the Princess nor the Forester has been given a name by the author, the answerer should supply instead the name of one of the King's three bosom-friends (or all three) and one of the Princess's (or all three)]

NORTH-COUNTRY MATTERS

In the most household-wordy play of all—

(1) Who was about to speak when the cock crew?

(2) Who said he once played the part of Julius Caesar?

(3) When was it that "the sheeted dead did squeak and gibber in the Roman streets"?

(4) Who deplored the "late innovation" of child-actors?

(5) Who found himself unable to say his prayers?

(6) Who bought an unction of a mountebank?

(7) Who said of whose condition that it might give rise to "dangerous conjectures in ill-breeding minds"?

(8) Who was told to put his bonnet to its right use?

(9) Who was described, by whom, as being "incapable of her own distress"?

(10) Who died saying, "The rest is silence"?

DAY AND NIGHT

*Where are—or who has—these references to the times of night
and day?*

(1) "Night's candles are burnt out, and jocund day
   Stands tiptoe on the misty mountain-tops"

(2) "Scarce had the sun dried up the dewy morn,
   And scarce the herd gone to the hedge for shade,
   When Cytherea, all in love forlorn,
   A longing tarriance for Adonis made"

(3) "The bawdy hand of the dial is now upon the
   prick of noon"

(4) "In the posteriors of this day which the rude
   multitude calls the afternoon"

(5) "In me thou seest the twilight of such day
   As after sunset fadeth in the west"

(6) "Much about cock-shut time"

(7) "The west yet glimmers with some streaks of day"

(8) "'Tis now the very witching time of night
   When churchyards yawn . . ."

(9) "The iron tongue of midnight hath told twelve"

(10) "What is the night?" "Almost at odds with
   morning, which is which?"

CONCLUSIONS

What have these particular lines in common, and in what plays do they occur?

(1) "Let us all ring Fancy's knell.
    I'll begin it—Ding, dong, bell."

(2) "Cry, Cock-a-doodle-do!"

(3) "Under the blossom that hangs on the bough"

(4) "To her let us garlands bring"

(5) "Seals of love, but sealed in vain, sealed in vain"

(6) "This life is most jolly"

(7) "Sweet lovers love the spring"

(8) "Youth's a stuff will not endure"

(9) "And we'll strive to please you every day"

(10) "While we lie tumbling in the hay"

ANSWERS

1

(1) Tubal in *The Merchant of Venice* likewise

(2) The two Mistresses of Alcibiades—Phrynia and Timandra—in *Timon of Athens*

(3) The Prince of Morocco—in *The Merchant of Venice*

(4) Margery Jourdain in *King Henry VI: Part Two*

(5) One of King Priam's Sons in *Troilus and Cressida*

(6) Aaron's offspring—*Titus Andronicus*

(7) An Apparition in *Macbeth*

(8) In *Pericles, Prince of Tyre*

(9) Captain Jamy in *King Henry V*

(10) The Welsh Captain in *King Richard II* (*Act II, Scene 4*)

2

(1) The father of Helena in *A Midsummer Night's Dream*

(2) Romeo's first love

(3) The fencing expert described by Claudius and Laertes in *Hamlet*

(4) Desdemona's mother's maid in *Othello*

(5) Caliban's mother in *The Tempest*

(6) The last in *King Henry V*'s list of noble English casualties at Agincourt

(7) Edgar's Foul Fiend in *King Lear*

(8) The Nurse's daughter who died in infancy—*Romeo and Juliet*

(9) Guests in Capulet's kitchen—*Romeo and Juliet*

(10) The father of Helena in *All's Well that Ends Well*

3

(1) Lady Faulconbridge in *King John*

(2) Orsino in *Twelfth Night*

(3) Juliet's Nurse

(4) Petruchio in *The Taming of the Shrew*

(5) Polonius in *Hamlet*

(6) Princess of France in *Love's Labour's Lost*

(7) Posthumus Leonatus in *Cymbeline*

(8) Brutus in *Julius Caesar*

(9) Macbeth

(10) Orlando in *As You Like It*

4

(1) *Measure for Measure*

(2) *Love's Labour's Lost*

(3) *Much Ado About Nothing*

(4) *The Winter's Tale*

(5) *Othello*

(6) *The Two Gentlemen of Verona.* (Note for the unwary:—*Romeo and Juliet* does *not* go to Milan.)

(7) *All's Well that Ends Well*

(8) *King John*

(9) *Pericles, Prince of Tyre*

(10) *The Tempest*

5

(1) The oldest Officer of the Watch in *Much Ado About Nothing*

(2) A Constable in *Love's Labour's Lost*

(3) One of the Watch in *Much Ado*

(4) A Sheriff's Officer in *King Henry IV*, *Part 2*

(5) An Executioner in *Measure for Measure*

(6) A Constable in *Measure for Measure*

(7) One of the Watch in *Much Ado*

(8) A Sheriff's Officer in *King Henry IV*, *Part 2*

(9) Chief Officer of the Watch in *Much Ado*

(10) In *King Henry V*

D

6

(1) Feste in *Twelfth Night*
(2) Gloster in *King Richard III*
(3) Hamlet
(4) Old Gobbo in *The Merchant of Venice*
(5) Ophelia in *Hamlet* in one of her songs
(6) King Lear
(7) Romeo
(8) King Lear
(9) Shylock
(10) Viola in *Twelfth Night*

7

(1) Orlando
(2) Oliver
(3) Orlando
(4) Celia
(5) Jaques
(6) Monsieur Le Beau
(7) The Exiled Duke
(8) Audrey
(9) Rosalind
(10) Phebe
   —all in *As You Like It*

8

(1) Falstaff (as narrated by Mrs. Quickly in *King Henry V*)

(2) Cleopatra

(3) The Fool in *King Lear*

(4) Desdemona in *Othello*

(5) Cloten in *Cymbeline* (*not* Macbeth who was slain first!)

(6) Portia in *Julius Caesar*

(7) Julius Caesar

(8) Cinna the Poet in *Julius Caesar*

(9) Polonius in *Hamlet*

(10) Coriolanus

9

(1) Maidservants of Antipholus of Ephesus in *The Comedy of Errors*

(2) King Lear's dogs

(3) Servants of Petruchio in *The Taming of the Shrew*

(4) Wenches loved (and disliked) by mariners in Stephano's song in *The Tempest*

(5) Favourites of King Richard II

(6) Falstaff's ragged recruits in *King Henry IV, Part 2*

(7) Swinge-bucklers recollected by Justice Shallow in *King Henry IV, Part 2*

(8) Followers of the rebel, Jack Cade, in *King Henry VI, Part 2*

(9) Three of the Musicians in Capulet's House, in *Romeo and Juliet*

(10) Fairy Attendants of Titania in *A Midsummer Night's Dream*

10

(1) Edgar in *King Lear*

(2) Jaques in *As You Like It*

(3) Sir Toby Belch in *Twelfth Night*

(4) Ophelia in *Hamlet*

(5) Bottom in *A Midsummer Night's Dream*

(6) Iago in *Othello*

(7) Justice Silence in *King Henry IV, Part 2*

(8) Autolycus in *The Winter's Tale*

(9) Sir Toby Belch in *Twelfth Night*

(10) Mamillius in *The Winter's Tale*

11

(1) The eunuch Mardian in *Antony and Cleopatra*

(2) Marcus Andronicus in *Titus Andronicus*

(3) Hamlet

(4) Hermia in *A Midsummer Night's Dream*

(5) Violets according to Perdita in *The Winter's Tale*

(6) Prince Hal according to Sir Richard Vernon in *King Henry IV, Part 1*

(7) Desdemona, so described by Iago in *Othello*

(8) Many cowards, according to Bassanio in *The Merchant of Venice*

(9) Titania and her changeling's mother in *A Midsummer Night's Dream*

(10) Imogen, so described by her husband, Posthumus Leonatus, in *Cymbeline*

12

(1) *The Tempest*

(2) *Hamlet*

(3) *King Henry VI, Part 2*

(4) *Coriolanus*

(5) *King Henry VI, Part 2*

(6) *King Richard II*

(7) *Pericles, Prince of Tyre*

(8) *The Winter's Tale*

(9) *The Tempest*

(10) *Timon of Athens*

13

(1) *King Henry V*

(2) *King John*

(3) *King Richard II*

(4) *King Henry VIII*

(5) *King Henry VIII*

(6) *King Henry V* (another in *King Richard III*)

(7) *King Richard III*

(8) *King Henry VI, Parts 1 and 2*

(9) *The Merry Wives of Windsor*

(10) *As You Like It*

14

(1) Quince, Bottom, Snug, Flute, Snout, Starveling

(2) Peter, Nick, —, Francis, Tom, Robin

(3) Carpenter, Weaver, Joiner, Bellows-mender, Tinker, Tailor

(4) Thisbe's Father; Pyramus; Lion; Thisbe; Pyramus's Father; Thisbe's Mother

(5) Prologue (and Prompter); Pyramus; Lion; Thisbe; Wall; Moonshine*

*Note: The ultimate and exact apportioning of the parts of Wall and Moonshine—between Snout and Starveling —is by no means explicit and amounts, indeed, to a matter for scholarly debate some midsummer morn at Stratford-on-Avon.

15

(1) *Measure for Measure*
(2) *Macbeth* (also, possibly, *King Lear*)
(3) *King Henry IV, Part 2*
(4) *Cymbeline*
(5) *Timon of Athens*
(6) *King Henry IV, Part 1*
(7) *The Winter's Tale*
(8) *King Henry VI, Part 2*
(9) *King Lear*
(10) *King Henry VIII*

16

(1) *The Winter's Tale*
(2) *The Winter's Tale*
(3) *As You Like It*
(4) *Cymbeline*
(5) *Much Ado About Nothing*
(6) *Hamlet*
(7) *The Taming of the Shrew*
(8) *Timon of Athens*
(9) *Macbeth*
(10) *Titus Andronicus*

17

(1) Charles in *As You Like It*

(2) Angelo in *The Comedy of Errors*

(3) Holofernes in *Love's Labour's Lost*

(4) Unnamed in *Timon of Athens*

(5) Unnamed in *The Tempest*

(6) Francis Flute in *A Midsummer Night's Dream*

(7) Dr. Caius in *The Merry Wives of Windsor*

(8) Barnardine in *Measure for Measure*

(9) Mardian in *Antony and Cleopatra*

(10) Unnamed in *Antony and Cleopatra*

18

(1) Puck in *A Midsummer Night's Dream*

(2) Feste in *Twelfth Night*

(3) Rosalind in *As You Like It*

(4) Imogen in *Cymbeline*

(5) Bottom in *A Midsummer Night's Dream*

(6) Edgar in *King Lear*

(7) Viola in *Twelfth Night*

(8) Belarius

(9) Guiderius

(10) Arviragus } as the supposed sons of the latter—

—all three in *Cymbeline*

19

(1) **Sir** Andrew Aguecheek so describes himself (*Twelfth Night*)

(2) Yorick, the dead jester, as described by Hamlet

(3) Cassio, in the opinion of Iago (*Othello*)

(4) Conrade, so described by Dogberry (*Much Ado*)

(5) Parolles, in the opinion of Bertram (*All's Well*)

(6) The Clown so describes himself (*All's Well*)

(7) The Recruit called Ralph Mouldy is so delineated by Justice Shallow (*King Henry IV, Part 2*)

(8) Lepidus is so regarded by Antony (*Julius Caesar*)

(9) The Clown with the figs and the asp is so described by the Guard (*Antony and Cleopatra*)

(10) A description of Agamemnon by Thersites (*Troilus and Cressida*)

20

(1) The late King Hamlet

(2) Brabantio (*Othello*)

(3) Egeus (*A Midsummer Night's Dream*)

(4) King Henry IV

(5) Baptista (*The Taming of the Shrew*)

(6) Leonato (*Much Ado*)

(7) Leontes (*The Winter's Tale*)

(8) Prospero (*The Tempest*)

(9) Duke Frederick (*As You Like It*)

(10) Cymbeline, by his previous Queen

21

(1) Lady Capulet

(2) Hermione in *The Winter's Tale*

(3) Volumnia

(4) The Queen in *Cymbeline*

(5) The Duchess of York

(6) Leah (*The Merchant of Venice*)

(7) The Nurse in *Romeo and Juliet*

(8) Constance in *King John*

(9) Queen Gertrude

(10) Lady Montague

22

(1) Bottom by Titania and her Fairies

(2) Trinculo and Stephano by Caliban in *The Tempest*

(3) Falstaff according to Sir Hugh Evans in *The Merry Wives*

(4)   Macbeth at his banquet

(5)   Hamlet at midnight

(6)   Sir Toby Belch in *Twelfth Night*

(7)   Cassio in *Othello*

(8)   Antony in *Antony and Cleopatra*

(9)   A sailor's wife described by one of the Three Witches in *Macbeth*

(10) Edgar said he did as Poor Tom in *King Lear*

23

Richard, Duke of Gloster, eventually King Richard III, is thus addressed or described by—

(1)   Queen Margaret in *King Henry VI, Part 3*

(2)   Lady Anne in *King Richard III*

(3)   ,,   ,,   ,,

(4)   ,,   ,,   ,,

(5)   Queen Margaret in *King Richard III*

(6)   ,,   ,,   ,,

(7)   ,,   ,,   ,,

(8)   ,,   ,,   ,,

(9)   Queen Elizabeth   ,,

(10) Richmond, later King Henry VII, in *King Richard III*

24

1. *Antony and Cleopatra*
2. *Hamlet*
3. *As You Like It*
4. *King Henry IV: Part 2*
5. *King Henry IV: Part 1*
6. *The Merchant of Venice*
7. *All's Well that Ends Well*
8. *Julius Caesar*
9. *Romeo and Juliet*
10. *King Henry VI: Part 1*

25

1. *Coriolanus*
2. *Much Ado About Nothing*
3. *All's Well that Ends Well*
4. *Love's Labour's Lost*
5. *Twelfth Night*
6. *Two Gentlemen of Verona*
7. *As You Like It*
8. *Hamlet*
9. *Macbeth*
10. *King Lear*

26

(1) Tybalt by Mercutio (*Romeo and Juliet*)

(2) Sir Andrew Aguecheek (*Twelfth Night*)

(3) Falstaff (*King Henry IV: Part 1*)

(4) Launce on his dog, Crab (*Two Gentlemen of Verona*)

(5) Bottom (*A Midsummer Night's Dream*)

(6) Nym by Pistol (*King Henry V*)

(7) Shylock (*The Merchant of Venice*)

(8) Apemantus by Timon of Athens

(9) Hamlet

(10) Thersites on Menelaus (*Troilus and Cressida*)

27

(1) In *Hark, Hark, the Lark,* the serenade in *Cymbeline*—also, arguably, in Sonnet beginning "When in disgrace . . ."

(2) In *Venus and Adonis*

(3) In Autolycus' song, "When daffodils begin to peer" in *The Winter's Tale*

(4) In *King Richard II*

(5) In *Romeo and Juliet*

(6) In *King John*

(7) In *Titus Andronicus*

(8) Imogen in *Cymbeline*

(9) Maria in *Twelfth Night*

(10) Macbeth

28

(1) *Cymbeline*

(2) *The Taming of the Shrew*

(3) *Much Ado About Nothing*

(4) *King Henry VIII*

(5) Pericles, *Prince of Tyre*

(6) *King Henry VI: Part 3*

(7) *King Henry VI: Part 3*

(8) *All's Well That Ends Well*

(9) *Twelfth Night*

(10) *Cymbeline*

29

(1) Benedick (*Much Ado About Nothing*)

(2) Touchstone (*As You Like It*)

(3) Oliver (*As You Like It*)

(4) Lysander (*A Midsummer Night's Dream*)

(5) The Duke (*Measure for Measure*)

(6) Sir Toby Belch (*Twelfth Night*)

(7) Angelo (*Measure for Measure*)

(8) Ferdinand (*The Tempest*)

(9) Florizel (*The Winter's Tale*)

(10) Bassanio (*The Merchant of Venice*)

30

(1) Imogen's according to Iachimo (*Cymbeline*)

(2) Orpheus's lute, according to Proteus (*Two Gentlemen of Verona*)

(3) The late King Hamlet's according to Horatio

(4) Prince Hal (*King Henry IV: Part 2*)

(5) Charles the Wrestler on the Banished Duke and his Followers (*As You Like It*)

(6) Portia's according to Bassanio (*The Merchant of Venice*)

(7) Anne Page by her Grandsire according to Sir Hugh Evans (*The Merry Wives of Windsor*)

(8) The dead King Duncan according to Macbeth

(9) Christopher Sly in the Induction (*The Taming of the Shrew*)

(10) "Who chooseth me shall get as much as he deserves." Belmont, The Prince of Morocco (*The Merchant of Venice*)

31

(1) Claudio according to the Clown (*Measure for Measure*)

(2) Malvolio by Maria (*Twelfth Night*)

(3) "The deserving woman" according to Iago (*Othello*)

(4) Fluellen, the Welshman (*Henry V*)

(5) In the Witches' Cauldron (*Macbeth*)

(6) Sir Toby Belch (*Twelfth Night*)

(7) The Apothecary (*Romeo and Juliet*)

(8) Adonis (*Venus and Adonis*)

(9) Sicinius by Coriolanus

(10) Caliban according to Trinculo (*The Tempest*)

32

(1) The Duke of Bourbon on England or the "isle of Albion" (*Henry V*)

(2) The wild boar in *Venus and Adonis*

(3) The bill of the ouzel-cock in Bottom's song (*A Midsummer Night's Dream*). Also he applies the epithet to a beard.

(4) War according to Gloster (*King Richard III*)

(5) Banquo's ghost according to Macbeth

(6) Thersites at Ajax (*Troilus and Cressida*)

(7) King Lear at Goneril

(8) The Queen on herself (*Cymbeline*)

(9) A humble-bee desired by Bottom (*A Midsummer Night's Dream*)

(10) Theseus on the play of "Pyramus and Thisbe" (*A Midsummer Night's Dream*)

33

(1) Benedick (*Much Ado About Nothing*)

(2) King Hamlet

(3) The King of France (*All's Well That Ends Well*)

(4) Othello

(5) Desdemona (*Othello*)

(6) Pandarus (*Troilus and Cressida*)

(7) Sir Toby Belch (*Twelfth Night*)

(8) Most of the Greeks around him by Thersites (*Troilus and Cressida*)

(9) Ophelia (*Hamlet*) and King Lear

(10) Edgar (*King Lear*) and Hamlet

34

(1) Charmian (*Antony and Cleopatra*)

(2) The cooks in Capulet's house, according to the Nurse (*Romeo and Juliet*)

(3) Gloster from the Bishop of Ely's garden in Holborn (*King Richard III*)

(4) The Porter's Man (*King Henry VIII*)

(5) Falstaff (*The Merry Wives of Windsor*)

(6) Arthur (*King John*)

(7) Titania for Bottom (*A Midsummer Night's Dream*)

(8) Mankind according to Falstaff (*King Henry IV: Part 2*)

(9) The Gardener (*King Richard II*)

(10) Simpcox the Impostor (*King Henry VI: Part 2*)

35

(1) Desdemona (*Othello*)

(2) Queen Katharine (*King Henry VIII*)

(3) Olivia (*Twelfth Night*)

(4) Hero (*Much Ado About Nothing*)

(5) The Princess of France (*King Henry V*)

(6) Julia (*Two Gentlemen of Verona*)

(7) Portia (*The Merchant of Venice*)

(8) Cleopatra (*Antony and Cleopatra*)

(9) Imogen (*Cymbeline*)

(10) Hermione (*The Winter's Tale*)

36

(1) Hippolyta in *A Midsummer Night's Dream*

(2) Titania in   ,,   ,,

(3) Tamora in *Titus Andronicus*

(4) *Hamlet* (Hamlet's mother)

(5) *King John* (King John's mother)

(6) *King Henry VIII*

(7) *King Henry V*

(8) *King Richard III*

(9) Queen to Richard II

(10) Cymbeline's Queen

37

Love's Labour's Lost

(1) Ferdinand, King of Navarre

(2) [Rosaline, Maria, Katharine]

(3) [Berowne, Longaville, Dumain]

(4) Holofernes

(5) Dull

(6) Costard

(7) Sir Nathaniel

(8) Jaquenetta

(9) Moth

(10) Don Adriano de Armado

38

(1) The ghost of Hamlet's Father according to Horatio

(2) Polonius

(3) "A little ere the mightiest Julius fell" according to Horatio

(4) Rosencrantz

(5) King Claudius

(6) Laertes

(7) Queen Gertrude on Ophelia's

(8) Osric

(9) Ophelia when drowning

(10) Hamlet

—all in *Hamlet*

(1) Romeo in *Romeo and Juliet*

(2) *The Passionate Pilgrim—not* in *Venus and Adonis*!

(3) Mercutio in *Romeo and Juliet*

(4) Don Adriano in *Love's Labour's Lost*

(5) Sonnet beginning, "That time of year thou mayst in me behold . . . "

(6) Gloster in *King Richard III*

(7) First Murderer in *Macbeth*

(8) Hamlet

(9) Theseus in *A Midsummer Night's Dream*

(10) Macbeth and Lady Macbeth

40

They are *last* lines of famous songs in the plays, beginning:

(1) "Tell me where is Fancy bred" (*The Merchant of Venice*)

(2) "Come unto these yellow sands" (*The Tempest*)

(3) "Where the bee sucks" (*The Tempest*)

(4) "Who is Silvia?" (*Two gentlemen of Verona*)

(5) "Take, O take those lips away" (*Measure for Measure*)

(6) "Under the greenwood tree" (*As You Like It*)

(7) "It was a lover and his lass" (*As You Like It*)

(8) "O mistress mine, where are you roaming" (*Twelfth Night*)

(9) "When that I was and a little tiny boy" (*Twelfth Night*)

(10) "When daffodils begin to peer" (*The Winter's Tale*)